3 STEPS TO INCREDIBLE HEALTH!

GET STARTED NOW! WORKBOOK

JOEL FUHRMAN, M.D.

PUBLISHED BY

ቂቂ

Gift of Health Press

OTHER BOOKS BY JOEL FUHRMAN, M.D.

Eat To Live

Eat For Health

Disease-Proof Your Child

Cholesterol Protection For Life

Fasting and Eating For Health

Published by Gift of Health Press, Flemington, New Jersey.

Contact:
Joel Fuhrman, M.D.
4 Walter Foran Boulevard, Suite 409
Flemington, NJ 08822

Publisher's Note:
Keep in mind that results vary from person to person. Some people
have a medical history and/or condition that may warrant individual
recommendations and in some cases drugs and even surgery. Do not
start, stop, or change medication without professional medical advice,
and do not change your diet if you are ill or on medication except
under the supervision of a competent physician. Neither this, nor any
other book, is intended to take the place of personalized medical care
or treatment.

Printed in the United States of America

Design: Robyn Rolfes, Creative Syndicate, Inc.
Cover Design: Savita Naidu

Library of Congress Control Number: 2011904331

ISBN: 978-0-9799667-9-8

First Edition

ACKNOWLEDGEMENTS

I thank my entire staff at DrFuhrman.com for the ideas and contributions to this workbook, especially Michael Mantz, M.D.

Contents

Introduction. 1

CHAPTER 1 A Review of Core Concepts 3

This section reinforces and explains the core concepts
making sure you understand the main points that were
brought up in the book and videos.

CHAPTER 2 Definitions 21

Many of the terms brought up in the books and videos
may be foreign to you. This section will help explain
some of the more difficult terms that are discussed.

CHAPTER 3 Exercises with Food 29

These are real world assignments such as buying,
preparing, and eating certain foods. The exercises
are designed to reinforce key points covered in the
books and to help retrain your food preferences.

CHAPTER 4 Action Plan For Your Success 39

This is your personal journal that encourages you to
get started the right way by reviewing your current
health statistics, building your motivation, setting
goals and planning for success.

CHAPTER 5 Tips and Tricks 55

Benefit from thousands of others who have
achieved incredible health with this program.

CHAPTER 6 Common Questions and Answers 61

Make sure you have all of your questions answered.

CHAPTER 7 Test Your Knowledge 77

These questions are designed to be challenging
(so don't worry if you get a few wrong) and include
short-answer and fill in the blank type of questions.

The Last Word 84

Answer Key to the test questions. 85

References 89

INTRODUCTION

Congratulations! You are taking a huge step to transforming your health and your entire life by investing your time and effort to learn more and more about my "nutritarian" eating style. This workbook works side-by-side with the *3 Steps To Incredible Health* book, transforming your learning from passive reading to active participation. No matter what your initial reason for purchasing this program, by now you know you have an opportunity not just to lose weight, but to dramatically improve your life and enhance your healthy life expectancy. That means living longer in excellent health.

I have designed this workbook to help clarify and reinforce the key concepts that are presented in my *3-Steps To Incredible Health* book. Some repetition is intentional to make sure you understand how to apply the most important concepts.

Most importantly, use this booklet as a workbook, to write in, highlight and reinforce the concepts you learned from reading the books and watching the videos. Fill in your personal information and work out your strategy to reach incredible health in the Action Plan section. Let me know how you do, of course I want to hear about your success, but I also want to help you overcome any obstacle that may interfere with you achieving your goals. Hopefully the informational tools you have purchased and are studying and the extra support available at DrFuhrman.com will make sure you cannot fail. Here's to your achieving incredible health!

A REVIEW OF CORE CONCEPTS

A diet designed to create disease...

Americans consume less than ten percent of their calories from unrefined plant foods such as fresh fruit, vegetables, beans, raw nuts, and seeds. Instead, they eat a diet of mostly processed foods and animal products. These large amounts of micronutrient-deficient animal foods and processed foods are the cause of most chronic diseases that afflict Americans. These foods supply calories, and way too much salt, but little else. The typical modern diet does not contain significant amounts of micronutrients, like antioxidants and phytochemicals.

This dangerously low intake of unrefined plant foods is what guarantees weakened immunity to disease, frequent illnesses, and a shorter lifespan. If this deficiency is not addressed, rates of cancer, heart disease, diabetes, auto-immune disease, degenerative illnesses, and obesity will continue to increase.

Consuming more of all the wrong things...

FOOD CONSUMPTION CHANGES IN THE UNITED STATES OVER THE LAST 100 YEARS		
	1900	**2000**
Sugar	5 lbs/yr	170 lbs/yr
Soft Drinks	0	53 gallons/yr
Oils	4 lbs/yr	74 lbs/yr
Cheese	2 lbs/yr	30 lbs/yr
Meat	140lbs/yr	200 lbs/yr
Homegrown Produce	131 lbs/yr	11 lbs/yr
Calories	2100	2757

The result is that we have become fatter and heart attacks and cancers have skyrocketed upwards in the last hundred years. Our society has evolved to a level of economic sophistication that allows us to eat ourselves to death.

We certainly have better sanitation and less infectious diseases, but we have replaced these diseases with diseases of nutritional ignorance. A diet centered on milk, cheese, pasta, bread, fried foods, sugar-filled snacks and drinks lays the groundwork for obesity, heart disease, stroke, cancer and diabetes.

Eating ourselves to death...

- 2/3 of adult Americans over the age of 20 are overweight or obese.[1]

- 9 million American children are currently obese.[2]

- 200 million Americans have a diet-related chronic illness.[3]

- Being overweight is the number one reason why people age faster than they should and die sooner than they should.[4]

- Heart Attacks, Strokes and Cancer account for approximately 60% of all deaths in the US today.[5]

Cancer: 22.0%

Heart Disease: 30.4%

Strokes (Cerebral Vascular Accidents) 7.4%

Almost half of all people in the U.S. are taking at least one prescription medicine and one in six are taking three or more medications. Prescription drug expenditures have risen at least 15 percent every year since 1998.[6]

Heart attacks, diabetes, strokes, cancer and dementia are virtually unheard of in populations that eat a plant based diet rich in fruits, vegetables, legumes and whole grains and low in animal fat and protein. In these same populations, when people change their diet and consume a Standard American Diet, the incidence of all these chronic diseases rapidly approaches that in America.[7]

UNREFINED PLANT FOODS ARE KEY TO
DISEASE RESISTANCE, HEALTH, AND LONGEVITY.

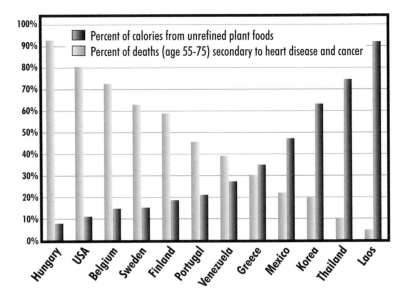

■ Percent of calories from unrefined plant foods
□ Percent of deaths (age 55-75) secondary to heart disease and cancer

This graph demonstrates that populations that consume more unrefined plant foods have much less heart disease and cancer. Unfortunately, this was based on World Health Association statistics from 1970 (food consumption data collected during the decade 1960 – 1970) and today there are no longer any countries that eat as much produce. Nowhere in the world today can we find a society that combines economic wealth with a high intake and variety of unrefined plant foods.

Increasing your intake of high-nutrient vegetables and fruits is critical to disease resistance, disease reversal and a long healthy life. As high-nutrient, unrefined, unprocessed plant foods increase in the diet, heart disease and cancer rates fall dramatically. Heart attacks and the most common cancers are found in rich societies where nutritional extravagance is the rule and fewer vegetables are consumed.

Dr Fuhrman's Health Equation: H = N/C

Your future Health (H) will increase as your
Nutrient (N)* to Calorie (C) ratio increases.

* Nutrient (N) refers to *micro*nutrients.

The secret to a long life and disease reversal is to eat a
diet lower in calories but higher in nutrients. It is all about
nutrient bang per caloric buck. This is illustrated by my
health equation. Your health is predicted by your nutrient
intake divided by your intake of calories or H = N / C.

This simple mathematical formula is the basis of nutritional science and nutritional healing. For you to be in
excellent health, your diet must be nutrient-rich (micronutrients) and you must not overeat on calories (macronutrients).

The nutrient density in your body's tissues is proportional
to the nutrient density of your diet. When your body's cells
have adequate micronutrient density, the body's ability to
self-repair and resist disease is heightened.

The key of this high-nutrient approach is this: You
achieve superior health and permanent weight control by
eating more nutrient-rich foods and fewer high-calorie, low-
nutrient foods. It works because the more high-nutrient food
you consume, the less low-nutrient food you desire. Since the
desire for these unhealthful foods will naturally diminish,
what you need to do is focus on learning how to enjoy eating
more high-nutrient food.

Which foods have the highest nutrient-per-calorie density?

To answer this question, I have ranked the nutrient levels of many common foods in the table below using my Nutrient Density Scores This scoring system assigns a score to a variety of foods based on how many nutrients they deliver to your body for each calorie consumed. The highest score a food can get is 100.

The scores are a simple way to help you identify and eat larger amounts of high-nutrient foods. Of course, avoid foods with negative scores as they have detrimental health effects. The higher the number and the greater percentage of nutrient-rich foods in your diet, the better your health will be. How do the foods you eat rate?

DR. FUHRMAN'S NUTRIENT DENSITY SCORES

Mustard greens	100	Iceberg lettuce	10
Watercress	100	Pistachio nuts	9
Kale	100	Cucumber	9
Turnip greens	100	Sweet potato	9
Collard greens	100	Green peas	7
Brussels sprouts	90	Almonds	7
Bok choy	85	Pineapple	7
Spinach	82	Avocado	6
Arugula	77	Cashews	6
Cabbage	59	Apple	5
Flaxseed	55	Mango	5
Broccoli	52	Peanut butter	5
Cauliflower	51	Corn	4
Romaine	45	Bananas	3
Green bell pepper	41	Brown rice	3
Onions	37	Oatmeal	3
Asparagus	36	White potato	2
Strawberries	35	Salmon	2
Mushrooms	35	Skim milk	2
Tomato	33	Low-fat plain yogurt	2
Pomegranate	30	Whole wheat bread	2
Carrots	30	Olive oil	2
Blueberries	27	Apple juice	1
Orange	27	White bread	1
Grapes	24	Chicken breast	1
Edamame	21	Eggs	1
Cherries	21	White pasta	1
Tofu	20	Shrimp	1
Sesame seeds	19	Ground beef, 85% lean	-4
Sunflower seeds	16	Feta cheese	-5
Artichoke	16	Low-fat cheddar cheese	-6
Lentils	14	Potato chips	-9
Cantaloupe	12	French fries	-9
Peaches	11	Vanilla ice cream	-9
Kidney beans	11	Cola	-10
Walnuts	10		

Fill up on nutrient-rich food

A human stomach can hold about one liter of food. Fill your liter with high-nutrient,-low calorie foods and you will prevent yourself from overeating and taking in too many calories.

400 CALORIES

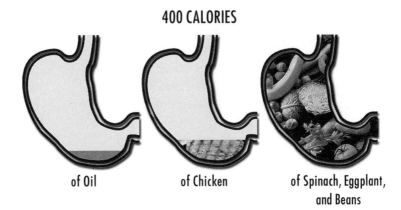

of Oil   of Chicken   of Spinach, Eggplant, and Beans

The images of these three stomachs are filled with the same amount of calories, but one with oil, one with chicken, and one with vegetables. The stomachs with oil and chicken have a great deal of room in them, room that can enable you to easily overeat on low-nutrient, high calorie foods. Filling your stomach with high-nutrient foods is critical to acquiring and maintaining a healthy weight.

A rule of thumb to remember: to lose more weight, and for better health, eat more high-volume, low-calorie foods. These are relatively "unlimited foods". Eat as much as you want of these foods (as long as you don't overeat). The greater the proportionyou eat of these foods, the faster you will arrive at your desired weight and also achieve incredible health.

High nutrient-low-calorie foods that can be eaten in nearly unlimited quantities (without overeating, of course):

All Raw Vegetables

Lettuce, Watercress, Arugula, Spinach, Tomatoes, Peppers, Carrots, Cucumbers, Cabbage, Zucchini, Snow Pea Pods, Onions

Green Cooked Vegetables

Brussels Sprouts, Kale, Collards, Bok Choy, Broccoli, Cabbage, Spinach, Swiss Chard, Asparagus, String Beans

Non-Green, Low Calorie, Cooked Vegetables

Cauliflower, Carrots, Eggplant, Mushrooms, Onions, Tomatoes, Peppers, Beets,

Fresh Fruits

Berries, Melons, Oranges, Apples, Cherries, Pineapple, Pears, Grapes and many more

Beans

Lentils, Split Peas, Black Beans, Kidney Beans, Adzuki Beans, Chick Peas, Bean Sprouts, Edamame

It's a matter of EMPHASIS

Most health authorities today are in agreement that we should add more servings of healthy fruits and vegetables to our diet. I disagree. Thinking about our diet in this fashion doesn't adequately address the problem. Instead of thinking of adding protective fruits, vegetables, beans, seeds and nuts to our disease-causing diet, *these foods must be mostly what you eat, the main focus of the diet itself.*

Once we understand this concept, then we can add a few servings of foods that are not in this category to the diet each week, and use animal products as condiments or small additions to this naturally nutrient-rich diet if desired.

DR. FUHRMAN'S FOOD PYRAMID

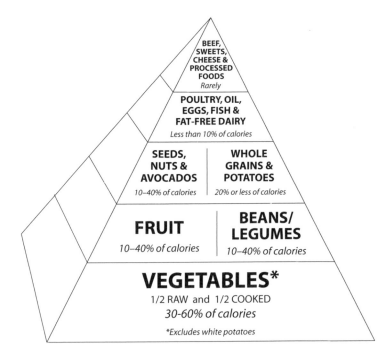

BEEF, SWEETS, CHEESE & PROCESSED FOODS
Rarely

POULTRY, OIL, EGGS, FISH & FAT-FREE DAIRY
Less than 10% of calories

SEEDS, NUTS & AVOCADOS
10–40% of calories

WHOLE GRAINS & POTATOES
20% or less of calories

FRUIT
10–40% of calories

BEANS/ LEGUMES
10–40% of calories

VEGETABLES*
1/2 RAW and 1/2 COOKED
30-60% of calories
*Excludes white potatoes

In a food pyramid, the foods that are consumed in the highest quantity become the base. However the standard American food pyramid—the source of most Americans' first understanding of health and nutrition—doesn't put nutrient-rich food at its base. This is one reason why so many Americans are confused about nutrition and plagued by obesity and preventable diseases.

My food pyramid is designed to achieve a healthy population and, if adopted by most Americans, would save millions of people's lives each year, and end our costly and tragic health care crisis. For superior health, we must eat more nutrient-rich foods and fewer calorie-rich foods. Therefore, the tip of the pyramid, the foods that should be consumed very rarely, will be the foods lowest in nutrients, such as processed foods like chips and cookies. This means the base of my pyramid is composed of the most nutrient-rich plant foods. When the nutritional landscape of America is shaped by nutrient density as represented in the pyramid above, we will have dramatically extended our healthy life expectancy and will see health care costs plummet.

Simply this means, eat lots of high-nutrient, natural plant foods: vegetables, fruits, beans, nuts and seeds. Eat much less or no animal products and eat much less or no foods that are completely empty of nutrients or toxic for the body, such as sugar, sweeteners, white flour, processed foods, refined oils, and fatty fast foods. Learn to trust the amazing power of the body. *If given half a chance, the body will heal itself*—with food as the catalyst.

Start with the Daily 5 healthy habits:

1) A large salad every day

2) At least a half-cup serving of beans/legumes in soup, salad or a dish once daily

3) At least 3 fresh fruits a day

4) At least one ounce of raw nuts and seeds a day

5) At least one large (double-size) serving of steamed green vegetables daily

Avoid these 5 most deadly foods:

1) Barbeque, processed meats or commercial red meat

2) Fried foods

3) Full-fat dairy (cheese, ice cream, butter, whole milk or 2% milk) or trans fat (margarine).

4) Soft drinks, sugar or artificial sweeteners

5) White flour products

TOP 30 FOODS

To make it easy for you to find the very best foods, I've listed my Top 30 Super Foods. These foods are associated with protection against cancer and a long healthy life. Include as many of these foods in your diet as you possibly can.

You are what you eat.
To be your best, you must eat the best!

NUTRIENT DENSITY SCORES OF THE TOP SUPERFOODS

Collard Greens, Mustard Greens, Turnip Greens	100
Kale	100
Watercress	100
Brussels Sprouts	90
Bok Choy	85
Spinach	82
Arugula	77
Cabbage	59
Broccoli	52
Cauliflower	51
Romaine Lettuce	45
Green & Red Pepper	41
Onions	37
Leeks	36
Strawberries	35
Mushrooms	35
Tomatoes and Tomato Products	33
Pomegranates/ Pomegranate Juice	30
Carrots/Carrot Juice	30/37
Blackberries	29
Raspberries	27
Blueberries	27
Oranges	27
Seeds: Flaxseed, Sunflower, Sesame, Hemp, Chia	25 (avg)
Red Grapes	24
Cherries	21
Plums	11
Beans (all varieties)	11
Walnuts	10
Pistachio Nuts	9

Low in calories and high in life-extending nutrients, green foods are your secret weapon to achieve incredible health. Scientific research has shown a strong positive association between the consumption of green vegetables and a reduction of all the leading causes of death.[8] Cruciferous vegetables—especially broccoli, brussel sprouts, cabbage, kale, bok choy, collards, watercress, and arugula—are loaded with disease-protecting micronutrients and powerful compounds that promote detoxification and prevent cancer.

Since cruciferous vegetables are your best weapons against cancer, include plenty of them in your diet.

kale • bok choy • cabbage • cauliflower • broccoli

broccoli rabe • broccoli sprouts • brussel sprouts

mustard greens • watercress • turnip greens • cauliflower

collards • arugula • radishes

The companion recipes from *3 Steps to Incredible Health* include numerous cruciferous vegetable soups and stews. Eat a good portion of these vegetables every day.

Overcoming bad habits

Let's face it: Bad habits and addictions can make dietary changes difficult. Fortunately, it only takes a few seconds of determination to say an emphatic "no" to the addiction and "yes" to your new healthful lifestyle. I have observed thousands of patients suffer through temporary discomforts while their bodies were eliminating the toxic aftermath of unhealthful diets. This is normal, and it is a small price to pay for the improved health and enhanced joy for life that will soon follow.

It may take time to reset your taste receptors to appreciate the more subtle flavors of whole natural foods, but your taste and flavor sensitivity will improve tremendously over time.

Three meals per day for maximum success

It is best to stick to a three-meal-per-day format, without snacking. Lots of people thrive on two meals per day, too. Unless you are an athlete or a physical laborer, you probably don't burn enough calories to justify snacking. If you eat enough at your regular meals, there should be no need for snacking.

Here are some helpful hints to combat snacking:

- Eat a salad or raw vegetables with a dip to start both lunch and dinner.

- Keep lots of frozen fruits and vegetables and pre-washed fresh foods in your home.

- Have cooked greens or soups with greens at every lunch and dinner.

- Don't eat after 8:00 p.m.

- Have a fruit-based dessert after dinner, then clean the kitchen, clean your teeth, and end eating for the day.

One of the most radical adjustments you have to make in following this high-nutrient diet-style is forgetting what you consider a normal portion size. Typical portion sizes are far too small for this plan. You will have new appreciation for this way of eating as your taste buds acclimate and you begin to eat more food than you are used to while obtaining your ideal weight. Get ready to discover that eating much larger amounts of the right foods—high-nutrient foods—is the secret to long-term weight loss and great health.

Eight Important Core Concepts:

1. Consuming calories without the presence of antioxidants, vitamins, and phytochemicals leads to a build-up of waste products in our cells. So when you eat white bread or other processed foods, the body can't remove normal cellular wastes that build up without the presence of a significant level of plant-derived anti-oxidant and phytochemical nutrients. When our cells don't have the raw materials needed for normal function it ages us prematurely and causes disease.

2. The most consistent and proven concept in the history of nutritional science is that the combination of high nutrient intake + lower caloric intake promotes disease resistance and longevity. It is the basis for my **health equation: Health = Nutrients/Calories.** What this means is that your health will improve as you eat high nutrient foods as a larger portion of your caloric intake (aka foods with a high nutrient density) and fewer foods with a low nutrient per calorie density. Avoid low-nutrient foods.

3. The foods highest in life-extending micronutrients and lowest in calories are green vegetables. They form the basis of my nutritarian diet. If you are overweight, the more greens you eat, the less of everything else you eat, the thinner and healthier you become.

4. The key component to reach incredible health is to eat more vegetables, fruits, nuts/seeds, beans and other nutrient-rich foods. As you eat larger amounts of these protective foods you will meet your body's micronutrient needs and naturally reduce the amount of animal products and processed foods in your diet without gimmicks, calorie counting, or portion control.

5. The major risk factors that lead to heart disease don't have to happen; they can be entirely prevented with dietary

and lifestyle interventions. The protection received from lowering one's blood pressure, weight, and cholesterol while removing atherosclerotic plaque with nutrition (and not with drugs) gives one dramatic protection against the development of heart disease.

6. White flour, other refined grains such as sweetened breakfast cereals, soft drinks, other sweets and even fruit juices are weight-promoting and not only lead to diabetes, but can also raise triglycerides and cholesterol levels, increasing heart attack risk. They comprise 62% of the calories in the typical Standard American Diet (SAD).

7. It's important to note that high salt intake deadens your taste buds to the subtle delicious flavors found in natural foods. So when you first reduce your salt intake, expect that some of the recipes may taste bland to you. Fortunately, your taste buds adjust to taking in less sodium by becoming more sensitive, so that natural foods will increase in flavor. Your ability to taste, not just sodium more intently, but also the subtle deliciousness of natural foods increases. This happens over time and it takes about 6-12 weeks on a low salt diet below 1000 – 1200 mg a day for this change to occur. I recommend keeping your sodium total to less than 1000 – 1200 mg a day and to not eat more than one food serving per day that has added salt, with less than 400 mg of extra salt a day, other than the naturally occurring sodium in natural plants.

8. When you lower LDL cholesterol with drugs you reduce your risk of dying from a heart attack somewhat, however when you lower your LDL with superior nutrition, which also lowers your blood pressure and normalizes your weight, you increase the anti-inflammatory micronutrients in your tissues. This allows virtually everybody to avoid heart disease completely and substantially lower or eliminate the risk of getting other diseases, such as diabetes and cancer.

DEFINITIONS

Advanced Glycation End Products (AGEs) — substances formed in which a sugar molecule binds to either a protein or fat molecule. AGEs have a pro-inflammatory effect on the body and love to damage the inner lining of blood vessels. They have been implicated in many chronic diseases, such as heart disease, diabetes, Alzheimer's disease and cancer. Common ways of producing AGEs in food are the browning of foods caused by high-temperature baking and the searing of meats.

Amino acids — the building blocks of protein. Amino acids are combined into larger and larger units to create proteins in our body.

Antioxidants — micronutrients that have the ability to help prevent the oxidation of your cells. Oxidation like the rusting of metal or the rotting of foods (like the browning of a cut apple or a banana that's been peeled and left out) occurs in our cells from the buildup of free radicals that can damage and eventually kill our cells. Antioxidants are substances that have the ability to help prevent this damage.

Atheromas — lipid (fat) deposits inside the walls of blood vessels.

Atherosclerotic plaque — fatty deposits that can line, harden and narrow the body's arteries.

Caloric density — how many calories there are in a given volume or weight of food. For example, any oil contains about 4100 calories for each liter (unit of volume) or 3900 calories for each pound (unit of weight) thus it has a very high caloric density, while green vegetables contain about 200 calories per liter or 100 calories per pound and thus have a very low caloric density.

Cardiac Angiography — a procedure where a thin hollow tube (a catheter) is inserted through the skin into an artery in the groin or the arm and guided to the openings of the coronary blood vessels. Using X-ray equipment and contrast (iodine solution that makes clearer x-ray images) images of the coronary vessels are produced (called an angiogram) to reveal any significant blockages.

Cardiac Stress Testing — a procedure where a patient's heart is stressed either by exercise or by medications that simulate exercise. While the heart is stressed, ECG (i.e. EKG) tracings (measures the electrical activity of the heart) and blood pressure checks are done looking for abnormalities. Finally, a radiotracer can be injected into the patient to allow a special camera to take pictures of the patient's heart and coronary arteries.

Cardiac Bypass Surgery — a procedure where blood is rerouted (bypassed) around a clogged coronary artery by taking a segment of a healthy blood vessel from another part of the body and making a detour around the blocked part of the coronary artery.

Carotenoids — red, orange, and yellow fat soluble pigments (think of tomatoes, red and yellow bell peppers, etc) found in plants that are powerful anti-cancer phytochemicals.

Congestive heart failure — Damage to the heart over time can lead to problems that affect the heart's ability to pump your blood effectively and to supply sufficient blood flow to meet your body's needs. This pump failure creates a back-up or congestion of fluid in your body's tissues.

Coronary artery disease — like any other organ in the body the heart has blood vessels that feed it nutrients/oxygen- rich blood. These vessels are called your coronary arteries. When we eat lots of processed foods and animal products these vessels eventually build up plaque, become inflamed and eventually reduce blood flow and oxygen delivery, leading to chest pains.

Diabetes Type 1 — usually presents in children. A form of diabetes where the body's immune system attacks its own pancreatic cells that produce insulin. Over time the destruction becomes so great that the person's ability to produce insulin becomes damaged. This results in elevated blood sugar levels and necessitates the use of exogenous insulin which is typically injected.

Diabetes Type 2 — usually presents in adulthood, but unfortunately due to excess body fat, is presenting earlier and earlier. It's a form of diabetes where the body's own cells become resistant to its insulin and thus more insulin is required. The pancreas compensates by pushing out more insulin, but over time the resistance builds up so much that the pancreas can't overcome it and the result is an elevation of blood sugar levels.

Dopamine — a neurotransmitter associated with movement, attention, learning, and the brain's pleasure and reward center. It is the primary chemical responsible for the temporary hit of pleasure one gets from eating concentrated calories.

EPA/DHA — long chain fatty acids built from the shorter chain omega 3 fatty acids. Both play many vital roles in our body, including mood regulation and mental acuity. Some people lack sufficient enzymes (especially with aging) to convert enough of the shorter chain omega 3 fatty acids into these longer chain fatty acids, so often supplementation is indicated.

Free radicals — normal atoms or molecules have paired electrons (think of electrons as needing to be married). If an electron loses its "partner", it becomes irritable and makes the atom/molecule highly reactive (aka a free radical). The free radical wants to pair up the "lonely" electron and will steal electrons from your healthy cells to do so and damage your healthy cells in the process. This process creates premature aging and disease especially heart disease and cancer.

Glucose — simple sugar that is used for energy production by your cells.

Glycogen — storage form of glucose found in your liver and muscle tissue.

Glycolysis — (glyco = sugar, lysis = to break) breakdown of glycogen back to glucose again to meet the body's needs for energy and to regulate the glucose level in the body's bloodstream.

Gluconeogenesis — (gluco = sugar, neo = new, genesis = birth/origin) the creation of glucose from amino acids. This is another way the body can help regulate the amount of glucose in its bloodstream when glycogen stores are insufficient.

Heart attack/cardiac arrest/myocardial infarction — the interruption of blood supply to part of the heart causing some heart/cardiac cells to die. Most commonly due to the blockage of a coronary artery that occurs when a lesion/plaque from that artery becomes inflamed, unstable and ruptures leading to the formation of a clot (thrombus), blocking blood flow and literally starving the cells of oxygen that normally receive blood flow from that coronary vessel.

Insulin — a hormone made by the pancreas whose main function is to help transport glucose out of your blood stream into the body's cells, supplying them with an energy souce.

Isothiocyanates (ITCs) — perhaps the most powerful anti-cancer phytochemicals in all foods. They are created when you chew, chop, blend, or puree cruciferous vegetables.

Lumen — the open inside channel of a vessel (imagine you are sliding inside an encased waterslide—you're sliding in the lumen of that waterslide).

Macronutrients — a class of 4 nutrients that includes protein, carbohydrates, and fat. These nutrients contain calories and are eaten in excess by most people. Water is the fourth macronutrient and the only one that does not contain calories.

Micronutrients — a class of nutrients that includes vitamins, minerals, antioxidants, and phytochemicals that contain no calories and are essential for our body's health, including strengthening our immune system and self-healing/repair systems.

Neurotransmitters — chemical messengers in the nervous system that permit nerve cells to communicate; examples include dopamine, serotonin, and acetylcholine.

Omega 3 fatty acids — essential fatty acids that the body needs to consume for proper health. They have an anti-inflammatory effect on the body and are beneficial to the heart, blood vessels, and nervous system (including the brain). They are not plentiful in our food supply except for some fatty fish. Eating dark green leafy vegetables, raw walnuts, hemp seeds, chia seeds, edamame, and flax seeds are plant sources to help get your daily requirements of these healthy fats.

Omega 6 fatty acids — essential fatty acids that the body also needs to consume for proper health. However, they tend to have a pro-inflammatory effect on the body if over-consumed, especially when consumed as oils and animal fats, which tend to be overeaten by people eating the standard diet.

Peripheral vascular disease — the same process as coronary artery disease except it happens in the peripheral blood vessels; most commonly the vessels in your legs.

Phytochemicals — ("phyto" = plant, chemicals) Micronutrients found in plant foods (and deficient in animal and processed foods) that have a wide range of beneficial effects on your body and are the largest micronutrient components found in natural foods and the major micronutrient components our bodies need to optimize immune system function and defenses against cancer.

Serotonin — a neurotransmitter associated with sleep, memory, appetite, mood, sensory perception, and temperature regulation. It is the primary chemical manipulated by antidepressant drugs like Prozac and Paxil and thus has a large role in promoting a sense of well being. Chronic ingestion of sugar lowers serotonin sensitivity (by abnormally spiking serotonin levels temporarily) in the brain and thus makes a person seek out artificial ways to boost serotonin (products with more and more sugar and refined carbohydrates) in order to compensate.

Statins — class of medications that block the production of cholesterol in your body.

Stroke — also known as a "brain attack." Your brain cells, like all cells in your body, need adequate blood flow in order to survive. This blood is brought to your cells through the arteries that feed them. If one of these vessels becomes blocked from a clot, the brain cells that were being served by that blocked vessel begin to suffer and die. This type of stroke is called an "embolic stroke" where the term embolic means that a piece of material entered the blood stream at some point upstream and then traveled downstream until it got stuck in an artery and obstructed it. The other type of stroke called a "hemorrhagic stroke" is when one of the feeding arteries in the brain ruptures and leaks out blood, most often over a larger area of the brain, that can cause paralysis and even death.

Trans-fat — is mainly a synthetic fat where extra hydrogen is added to an unsaturated fat to improve its shelf life, flavor, and functional properties. Unfortunately, these synthetic fats are foreign to the body's metabolism and wind up causing all kinds of mayhem to your cells. They may be the worst kind of fat for your health, as they are implicated in increasing your risks for heart disease, cancer, diabetes and depression. Look for and avoid any foods that list partially hydrogenated or just hydrogenated oils on their food labels.

EXERCISES WITH FOOD

If you are overwhelmed and don't know where or how to start, this is for you. Let's start putting some of the principles that you have learned into practice. These ten dietary exercises are the place to start. It is important that you think of these exercises in the same way that you think of exercises at the gym. When you go to the gym, you don't expect to suddenly build muscle; that takes time. You may not even enjoy going to the gym when you first start out. The enjoyment comes later, when you see your body starting to change.

Move down the exercise list. Perform each exercise for at least a week, and then move on to the next. You can still continue the prior exercises as you add additional exercise challenges on your journey to incredible health.

The most important element of these exercises is performing them every single day. Doing them daily will not only increase your enjoyment of healthful foods, but also will help you lose weight. In the beginning, you may continue eating some foods from your traditional diet, although you will probably be eating a lot less of them. Over time, you will be more comfortable eliminating your unhealthful food choices and replacing them with healthful ones because your palate will desire them.

A skill is a developed talent or ability, and being healthy is the result of several skills. The difficulty comes when you try to be proficient in all of those skills at once. Enjoying the taste of healthful food is a skill. Giving up old foods that you love in favor of new foods that you don't like requires multiple skills: abstinence and tolerance. These exercises isolate and target specific skill sets. They will help you avoid the anxiety that many feel when they give up their old way of eating all of a sudden. The method that I have developed is a purposeful and effective way to assist you in your transition to preferring a healthful approach to eating.

I also want you to keep a health journal; it has a proven record of enhancing success as documented in the scientific literature. Record your food intake, which exercises you are working on and your results. Review your health journal and make note of the transformation that has taken place as you go. Use the space in this book, or duplicate the pages in a notebook designed for that purpose. Check over your goals and update them if necessary and add any new goals that you might now have. For now, create a plan for the next 2 weeks on what your health goals are and how you want to accomplish these goals. Every two weeks make some new goals, log how much weight you lost (if that is one of your goals), how fit you've become and what other health-related accomplishments you've achieved. Keep track of your progress. Write down if you reached your goals and if not, what you plan to do better, so you can clearly see the benefits and results.

Exercise 1

Eat one-half pound of cut up raw vegetables and one-half pound of low-calorie fruits each day.

Try to do this exercise at the same time each day. I recommend eating the fruit at breakfast and the raw vegetables in the afternoon before dinner. The important thing is to do this exercise close to mealtime and not when you have a full stomach. Remember, your lunch should be light enough, so you are really hungry before dinner. It will make dinner more enjoyable if you are really hungry when you eat it.

The goal of this exercise is to eat a comfortable amount of raw vegetables, including tomatoes, red pepper, carrots, broccoli spears, celery, snow pea pods, and zucchini, and fruits, including fresh berries, cantaloupe, kiwi, and apple slices. Over time, see if you can comfortably increase the volume of food. Plus, if you want to eat more than a half of a pound of salad to begin dinner you can. You can use one of our healthy dressing recipes with these raw vegetables too, and you can even cut up the fruit and make a salad that has in it both fruits and lettuce, shredded cabbage, shredded carrots or beets, onion and tomato.

After eating all these raw vegetables and fruits, you may decide to eat less at dinner because you feel too full, but let that decision come naturally. Try not to overeat, but don't try to restrict yourself, either. Eat the amount that feels comfortable, and try to stop eating before you feel full. Stop when you're satisfied. Finding the difference between being satisfied and full is an important step in becoming a healthy eater.

❏ CHECK HERE WHEN YOU HAVE COMPLETED **EXERCISE ONE** FOR AT LEAST A WEEK

EXERCISE 2

The second exercise can be done at the same time as the first. While you are eating those fruits and vegetables, chew each mouthful until every piece of food is liquefied. This will take a considerable amount of time and will feel very different from how you are used to eating, but how you eat is very important. Eating slowly is the only way to gain all the nutrients that you want from the food. You can access the full nutrient load from the food by breaking open every single plant cell. Eating this way also will exercise your jaw and help you develop healthier gums and teeth. Remember: Chew, chew, and chew.

> ❏ CHECK HERE WHEN YOU HAVE COMPLETED
> **EXERCISE TWO** FOR AT LEAST A WEEK

EXERCISE 3

Take the half-pound of vegetables and half-pound of fruit that you are eating daily and increase them to one pound each per day. The pound of vegetables can be raw or cooked. Eating two salads daily—one of vegetables and one of fruit or whatever combination you feel like—is not too much. To help you meet your vegetable goal, eat a bowl of vegetable bean soup or a vegetable bean casserole each day. The recipes in *3 Steps to Incredible Health* can help you along the way. Try some of the delicious salad dressing recipes with your salads, or use them as dips for raw vegetables. One pound may seem like an overwhelmingly large amount of vegetables, but keep in mind one tomato can weigh half a pound, and other high water-content foods, such as cucumbers and peppers, add up the weight quickly. If you are starting to feel full, stop eating. Do not allow any of these exercises to encourage you to overeat or eat until discomfort.

> ❏ CHECK HERE WHEN YOU HAVE COMPLETED
> **EXERCISE THREE** FOR AT LEAST TWO WEEKS

Exercise 4

As you add more volume to your diet, also change the types of fruits and vegetables that you are eating. Alternate at least two different fruits and two different vegetables in your diet each week. Also, I encourage you as part of this exercise to try a fruit or vegetable that you rarely eat or have never tried. This is a good opportunity to see the palate stretching in action as you realize that your tastes can change. Especially seek out fresh pomegranates, shallots, fresh parsley and dill, various mushrooms, and other leafy greens in stews and main dishes, such as collards, mustard greens and broccoli rabe. All these foods have powerful effects to prevent cancer and repair any cell damage that could have occurred in the past that could lead to cancer. Grocery stores today have plenty of variety in their produce departments. They most likely contain something you have not yet discovered. Be adventurous; stretch your palate and your experience in an effort to have a more complete diet. Like all exercises, they require frequent practice in order to see results. Remember, it takes 15 times of eating a new food to develop a taste for it. This will also help give you better phytochemical variety which has health benefits and helps rid you of toxic hunger.

❏ CHECK HERE WHEN YOU HAVE COMPLETED
EXERCISE FOUR FOR A MONTH

EXERCISE 5

Make a point to eat a light lunch or a light breakfast each day. Eating one lighter meal without snacking before the next meal, either lunch or dinner, will increase your true hunger before that meal. Over time, this will help to teach you what true hunger feels like. The main exercise target here is to see if you can get back in touch with sensations of "true hunger," differentiating the sensations from "toxic hunger." Be patient because it may take some time (even a few months) for toxic hunger to go away. This exercise of trying to eat two main meals and one lighter meal, with no snacking will help you get in touch with your hunger symptoms. The point here is that hunger is the best sauce, in other words it will greatly enhance the pleasure when you do eat. Try to link together an entire week of high-nutrient eating, with no snacking, so you can lose the toxic hunger symptoms and begin the pleasurable sensation of true hunger.

❑ CHECK HERE WHEN YOU HAVE COMPLETED
EXERCISE FIVE FOR AT LEAST A WEEK

EXERCISE 6

Reduce your consumption of animal products (meat, eggs, and dairy products) to no more than one serving every other day. That means if you have some animal product during the day, make the next day completely vegan. Eventually, reduce the size of the animal product servings so when you do use them, it is not more than a few ounces to flavor a stew, soup or dish. Use the high-nutrient recipes in *3 Steps to Incredible Health* to replace animal products in your menus.

❑ CHECK HERE WHEN YOU HAVE COMPLETED
EXERCISE SIX FOR AT LEAST TWO WEEKS

Exercise 7

Remove white flour, sugar, and other sweeteners from your diet. For this exercise, no artificial sweeteners or low calorie sweeteners are allowed either. This means using fewer processed foods. Store-purchased products should be 100 percent whole grain and contain no sweetening agents. Remember, wheat flour means white flour, it must say 100 percent whole wheat or 100 percent whole grains. Sweeteners and white flour promote cancer, so it is wise to avoid them or only use them very occasionally. Obviously, for this two week exercise, you are making a commitment to have no sugar or other sweetening agents such as honey or maple syrup or even stevia for a full 2 weeks. Think you can do it?

This exercise, when continued for a few weeks, helps recondition your taste to enjoy the subtle flavors and sweetness in fruits and vegetables. What most people do not realize is that the continual intake of a diet rich in sweeteners deadens ones taste buds, so simple foods like strawberries no longer taste sweet. The only thing sweet should be fresh fruit. The purpose of this exercise is to break your addiction to sweets, so you control your dietary choices, and no longer have cravings.

❑ CHECK HERE WHEN YOU HAVE COMPLETED
EXERCISE SEVEN FOR AT LEAST TWO WEEKS

EXERCISE 8

The base of the nutritarian diet is green vegetables. If you do not consume cooked green vegetables on a daily basis let's change that today. Not only should you have lots of raw greens as discussed in the earlier exercises, but also make sure you now eat a large serving of cooked greens too. Delicious, yet mild tasting, green vegetables include green beans, sugar-snap peas, zucchini, asparagus and artichokes as well as broccoli, kale and much more. They are all great cooked with onions, scallions, garlic and mushrooms. You can sauté them in water, tomato juice, or other veggie juice, or with coconut water and sliced pineapple for a Hawaiian flavor. You can stew them with beans and vegetable juice, or enjoy them just steamed plain with or without a dip. Try lots of the green-based main dishes from the recipe section of the book and keep track of your favorites.

☐ CHECK HERE WHEN YOU HAVE COMPLETED
EXERCISE EIGHT FOR AT LEAST TWO WEEKS

EXERCISE 9

Decreasing one's sodium can be one of the most difficult things to do because salt is so addictive and because it deadens your taste buds, making food taste bland for up to 3 months before they revitalize themselves. I want you to avoid any sodium that is not in natural produce, except for 400 mg a day. That means you eat all produce, but if you have a piece of store-bought whole grain bread, or some tomato sauce or ketchup, you have to read the label and measure the amount used so you don't go over that 400 mg level. That will keep the total sodium in your diet under 1000 mg a day. Commit to this for a full week. Sustain it longer or even better, permanently if possible.

Remember to read labels as 80% of our sodium intake comes from pre-packaged foods rather than the salt shaker. Pay attention when eating your meals to the other flavors found in food besides saltiness. Increase the sourness and sweetness of your meals by using vinegars, lemon and fruits. Add interesting herbs and spices and no-salt spice mixtures. Then go back to a regular sodium day that you ate before the experiment a week later. Notice the difference in your taste buds. Record the experience of this experiment in your health journal. Then expand the number of days on a low sodium diet again focusing on the other flavors of foods rather than saltiness. Realize that your taste buds are being revitalized and will soon be able to taste things in a new way that will make unprocessed plant foods taste amazing. Again record your experiences in your health journal.

☐ CHECK HERE WHEN YOU HAVE COMPLETED **EXERCISE NINE** FOR AT LEAST TWO WEEKS

EXERCISE 10

Research and find two restaurants in your area that will cater to your nutritarian diet-style. This exercise involves going out to eat and still remaining on your nutritarian diet in two different places over a two week period. The first step is finding a restaurant that will have some healthy meal options. Calling ahead can be very helpful in this regard and you can ask questions on whether they will cater to your preferences. Many restaurants for breakfast offer fresh orange juice, oatmeal with raisins and fruit. For lunch and dinner, try to find a restaurant with a salad bar or even a market that has a salad bar and eating area. If they don't have a salad bar, order a double-size salad minus unhealthy items (cheese, bacon bits, etc) and have the dressing on the side. Use only a touch of commercial dressing, adding extra vinegar and lemon if you wish. See what vegetable options are on the menu, even if part of another dish and ask if you can have a double-sized portion of those. Make sure you clearly reiterate, not to use oil or salt and that you appreciate the staff for complying with your dietary requirements. You can always say, "doctor's orders". Avoid consuming soups in restaurants as they are almost always loaded with salt. It is also very important to ask the waiter not to bring over the tempting bread basket to the table.

☐ CHECK HERE WHEN YOU HAVE COMPLETED
EXERCISE TEN FOR AT LEAST TWO WEEKS

ACTION PLAN FOR YOUR SUCCESS

As you embark on your new dietary journey, keep in mind that there are three vital components to high-level health. Each of the three components—nutritional, physical, and social—must be considered.

Nutritional component — Make every calorie count as you strive for maximum nutrition. *3 Steps to Incredible Health* provides all of the information you need.

Physical component — Make physical exercise a part of your normal routine. Joining a gym is a great bonus, but learn to take advantage of all of your opportunities to exercise—such as taking the stairs instead of the elevator and, when possible, walking instead of riding. You may find that exercise is easier and more pleasurable as your health improves and you start losing weight. Remember to limit sitting. Try to work part of the day standing up.

Social component — Develop the confidence and self-esteem necessary to deal with unhealthful influences. A healthy mindset is a prerequisite for a healthy lifestyle, and the best way to develop it is to surround yourself with people who engage in and support your health.

Over time, your taste and food preferences change. You become more comfortable eating high-nutrient foods, and it will become second nature—the way you prefer to eat. This is a high-nutrient program, not a calorie-counting one.

Your Current Health Snapshot:

Now let's get a current snapshot of who you are and your current health statistics so that you can track your soon-to-be amazing path to incredible health and vitality.

NAME: . . . .

AGE: . . . .

START DATE WITH DR. FUHRMAN'S TEACHINGS: . . . .

STARTING WEIGHT: . . . .

WAIST MEASUREMENT: (AT UMBILICUS) . . . .

BLOOD PRESSURE: . . . .

LIST ANY HEALTH ISSUES YOU WOULD LIKE TO BE HELPED BY THIS PROGRAM: . . . .

. . . .

. . . .

. . . .

. . . .

. . . .

BLOOD LEVELS

TOTAL CHOLESTEROL:........

LDL: ....

HDL: ....

TRIGLYCERIDES: ....

VITAMIN D LEVELS: ....

GLUCOSE: ....

IF DIABETIC ADD HBA1C: ....

CURRENT PHOTO:

Finding Your Motivation

Starting a new program is both exciting and difficult. As humans we naturally want what is best for us, yet we also fear change. To overcome this fear you need to solidify your motivations for wanting to change your current lifestyle to a more vibrant and healthy one. Your motivations are the fuel to light the fire that is required for successful change from your current health habits to the healthiest habits that will propel you to a new level of health that you never dreamt was possible. With every great achievement comes some sacrifice and struggle and when we are struggling it's very helpful to have reminders as to why we are changing and what matters to us most.

On a scale of 1 to 10, rate the most compelling reasons you have for eating healthfully:

_____ I want to recover from a chronic illness, such as high blood pressure, diabetes, headaches or high cholesterol.

_____ I want to protect myself from developing a dangerous disease.

_____ I want to prevent the deterioration in health, physical, and mental abilities that are typically considered a normal part of aging.

_____ I want to lose weight and look and feel better.

_____ I want to increase my energy and reduce fatigue.

_____ I want to improve the health of my family.

_____ I want to improve my physical fitness.

_____ I want protection from frequent bouts of infectious disease.

_____ I want to have better digestion.

_____ I want to have better sexual enjoyment
and performance.

_____ I want to look and feel younger.

_____ I want to have a better emotional outlook on life.

_____ I want to live longer.

_____ I want to live without medical interference
and hospitalizations.

_____ I want to avoid surgery or prescription medication.

_____ I want to reduce my dependency on medication.

_____ I want to save money on health care and
prescription drugs.

Other reasons: _____

_____

_____

_____

_____

Each time you encounter some difficulty with the eating-style
described in these materials, each time you want to revert
back to your old ways of eating, each time you slip-up on the
program, each time you believe great health is unattainable
for you, come back and look at this page.

Creating your future with Goals

Now we are going to take your motivations a step further and create some specific goals to generate crystal clear targets for you to strive for. By writing down specifically what you want, you put into motion the forces that are necessary for achieving your desires.

Well constructed goals literally create the future in advance. The formula for creating successful goals is that they need to be specific, time dependent and they must have clear and measurable outcomes. For instance, "I want to look great and lose weight" does not meet the criteria of a well constructed goal. A better example would be "I want to lose 20 pounds in the next 6 weeks and be able fit into the size 6 jeans I wore in college." This second example is specific, has a timeline and a measurable outcome by which you can determine whether you have achieved your goal or not.

You can have all the knowledge and know all of the techniques but if you don't have a target to drive towards or compelling reasons why you are doing something then it is less likely you are going to get the most out of yourself. So alongside your goals you need to write down why you want to achieve them. You need to get absolutely clear on this. The why provides the fuel for you to accomplish your aspirations.

Many people erroneously believe that it's only a matter of willpower to change one's unhealthy habits to obtain a new and vibrant healthy lifestyle. Willpower is an unreliable emotional fuel that usually putters out over a short period of time. To be successful at making life long healthy changes you need knowledge, techniques, and a well constructed strategic plan to put the knowledge and techniques into action. Key parts of that strategic plan are your goals. So, list below at least 5 health-related goals and the reasons why you want to achieve them. Then review them on a scheduled basis, perhaps every week or maybe even every night. Lastly, goals should be adjusted and updated periodically, so be flexible and get excited about finally creating the future you've always dreamed of!

> *"The greater danger is not that your hopes are too high and you fail to reach them; it's that they're too low and you do."*
>
> —Michelango

GOAL 1)...

WHY: ....

....

GOAL 2)..

WHY: ....

....

GOAL 3)...

WHY: ....

....

GOAL 4)...

WHY: ....

....

GOAL 5)...

WHY: ....

....

The Benefits of Incredible Health

- Lose weight and look and feel the best you ever have

- Never suffer from a heart attack or stroke

- Avoid dementia in later life

- Dramatically reduce your chance of getting cancer

- Prevent and heal digestive problems such as reflux, indigestion, constipation, and hemorrhoids

- Prevent and often resolve erectile impotence, high blood pressure, and other circulatory impairments

- Prevent and reverse diabetes (Type 2) and high cholesterol, at first lessening the need for drugs and eventually resolving these conditions

- Age slower, live longer, and maintain youthful vigor, intelligence, and productivity into the later years

I. MOST IMPORTANT THINGS TO REMEMBER ABOUT EATING FOR INCREDIBLE HEALTH

1.

2.

3.

4.

5.

II. YOUR WEEKLY SHOPPING LIST

1.	26.
2.	27.
3.	28.
4.	29.
5.	30.
6.	31.
7.	32.
8.	33.
9.	34.
10.	35.
11.	36.
12.	37.
13.	38.
14.	39.
15.	40.
16.	41.
17.	42.
18.	43.
19.	44.
20.	45.
21.	46.
22.	47.
23.	48.
24.	49.
25.	50.

III. 3-DAY MEAL PLANNING

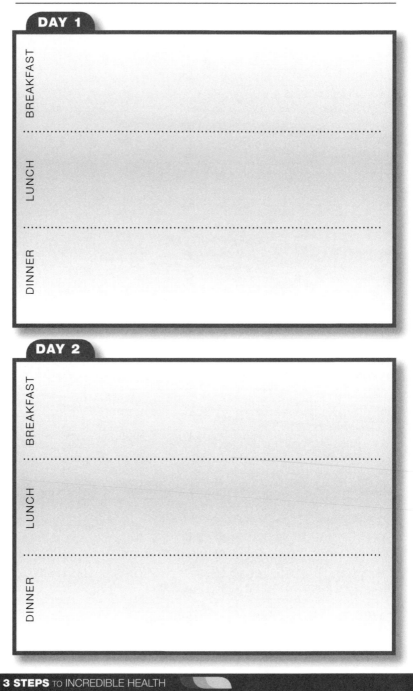

DAY 1

BREAKFAST

LUNCH

DINNER

DAY 2

BREAKFAST

LUNCH

DINNER

DAY 3

BREAKFAST

LUNCH

DINNER

IV. RECIPE PLANNING

SALADS AND SALAD DRESSINGS

INGREDIENTS

PREPARATION INSTRUCTIONS

SOUPS/STEWS

INGREDIENTS   PREPARATION INSTRUCTIONS

VEGETABLE-BASED MAIN DISH

INGREDIENTS   PREPARATION INSTRUCTIONS

SMOOTHIES

INGREDIENTS | PREPARATION INSTRUCTIONS

SORBETS AND DESSERTS

INGREDIENTS | PREPARATION INSTRUCTIONS

V. ACCEPTABLE PREPARED FOODS
OR RESTAURANT STRATEGIES

TOP 5 DO'S

1.

2.

3.

4.

5.

TOP 5 DON'TS

1.

2.

3.

4.

5.

VI. WEEKLY PLANNER

**FILL OUT YOUR WEEKLY PLANNER AND DECIDE WHEN YOU
WOULD DO THE FOLLOWING ACTIVITIES:**

Shop **(S)**   Cook **(C)**   Eat Leftovers **(EL)**

Exercise **(E)** *(be specific on the kind of exercise)*

	MORNING	AFTERNOON	EVENING
MON			
TUE			
WED			
THU			
FRI			
SAT			
SUN			

Don't forget to journal the physical component

As soon as you begin to lose some weight and start feeling better, usually once the withdrawal phase of the first week is over, start to increase your physical exercise intensity and do more than just walk. Exercise more vigorously and do something vigorous every day. In other words, do jumping jacks for 3 minutes or jog in place. At the beginning, just jog with your feet hardly lifting off the ground, but as the weeks and months progress, not only should you increase your duration, but as you pick your feet and knees up high off the ground, you can increase the intensity of the effort. Add other types of exercise too. Walk up and down stairs as part of your exercise program and look for opportunities during the day to walk extra flights of stairs. Do something every day, increasing the minutes of intense exercise you can tolerate.

A good way to start is to pick a song with a good beat and bounce around to the music shifting your weight from side to side as you bounce up and down. As you get in better shape you can jump off the ground as you hop from foot to foot, increasing the intensity of the combination dancing-jumping motion. Journal the amount of exercise you are able to accomplish, so you can note the improvement in your exercise tolerance as you eat healthier, lose weight and perform the food exercises.

It is also important for your long-term health to not sit all day long. Even if you are exercising regularly, it is still important to limit your sitting during the day. Try to stand when talking on the phone and put your laptop or paperwork elevated on a counter and work standing up part of the day as well. I sometimes place my laptop on a large overturned pot on my kitchen counter to bring it to a comfortable standing height. Limit sitting, maximize motion and try to be conscious of incorporating fitness into your everyday life.

TIPS AND TRICKS

Adopting a high-nutrient diet is a big change for most people, but clearly it is not an all-or-nothing plan. It is a journey toward taking control of your own health destiny. No matter what phase or level you start with, positive changes will provide rewards. Have fun, enjoy your food, and take control of your health. *3 Steps to Incredible Health* is all about empowering you with the knowledge and support you need to once again get back in touch with the natural wisdom of your body.

Eat a large, raw salad at least once a day. Put a big sign on your refrigerator that says, "Salad is the Main Dish". The amount of leafy lettuce and other leafy greens such as spinach, shredded cabbage and arugula in the salad should amount to at least 5 ounces.

Add other raw vegetables (besides the leafy greens) such as tomatoes, shredded carrots, cabbage, beets, snow peas, or raw broccoli to the salad so that the total of raw vegetables for the day amounts to at least 12 ounces of food.

Consume a double-portion serving of steamed green vegetables (at least 12 ounces a day). Vegetables such as asparagus, artichokes, kale, collards, broccoli, Brussels sprouts, green beans, baby bok choy, and other greens should be eaten every day. You can also do this by adding these greens to a soup or stew.

1. Eat a half cup to one cup of beans daily in a vegetable soup, on your salad, as an ingredient of a main dish or in a dip.

2. Eat at least one ounce of raw seeds or nuts daily. Try to use more seeds and less nuts.

3. Eat at least four fresh fruits daily. Try to eat some berries, cherries or other high-nutrient fruits regularly.

4. Have some fresh squeezed vegetable juice either by itself or part of your soup or stew base on most days.

5. Measure and control the amount of animal products consumed. Do not eat more than one serving of animal products a day and limit the size of the portion so it is less than four ounces. That means no larger than the size of a deck of cards. Then, as you move forward, try to move up to the next level of superior nutrition by reducing animal products further. It would be a significant health achievement if you do not have more than one small serving of animal products every other day. In other words, whether you have two eggs, chicken in your salad or soup, or a turkey sandwich on whole grain pita, make the next day a strict vegetarian day. Do not eat processed, barbequed or salted meats.

6. Reduce and measure your salt intake. Do not cook with salt in the home. Do not eat soup or sauces in restaurants; they are too high in sodium. Always order the dressing on the side and ask if the food can be prepared without the sauce. If you are using a packaged food, make sure the sodium content is not more than 400 mg, and make sure that this is the only sodium-extra food that you consume that day. In other words, limit your salt consumption to 400 mg per day in addition to the natural sodium found in all the unsalted produce and other dishes you eat each day.

7. Get most of your starch intake from beans, carrots, peas, squash and sweet potato, not from flour products and white potato or white rice. Do not eat any white flour products. If you're using bread and pasta, use limited amounts, not more than one serving per day and, of course, make sure it is 100 percent whole grain.

8. Limit your consumption of oil to one tablespoon daily. Oil is a fattening, low-nutrient food, so the less you use the better. If you eat something cooked with oil, make sure you do not use oil on your salad that day.

9. Sweets and baked goods also drive up blood pressure. Refined carbohydrates drive up glucose levels which in turn drives up the amount of advanced glycation end products (AGEs) in your body (high levels of glucose in your blood like to bind to proteins in your blood forming these toxic AGEs) and makes your body oversecrete insulin. This in turn causes both oxidative stress and a pro-inflammatory state. It's as if you're turning up the heat and increasing "the rust formation" in your cells especially the cells that line the walls (called endothelial cells) of your blood vessels, leading to atherosclerosis which in turn creates higher blood pressure, higher pulse pressure, and greater risk of heart attacks and strokes.

10. Blood pressure medications simply lower blood pressure but don't address the predominate problem that causes heart attacks: atherosclerosis which creates stiff blood vessels and inflammation that eventually can lead to a clot and a heart attack. Blood pressure medications also have a lot of negative side effects including fatigue, lightheadedness/dizziness which can lead to falls and hip fractures, erectile difficulties/impotency, some like beta blockers can predispose people to diabetes and sometimes premature death.

11. Your heart receives blood from its own vessels (coronary arteries) during its diastolic phase when it's relaxed (think of it like how we eat best when we are relaxed) and thus a proper diastolic blood pressure is essential for the heart to "get fed" properly. Excessive use of some blood pressure medications can lower diastolic blood pressure too low, which essentially begins to decrease the return of blood during the resting phase, leading to serious rhythm disturbances.

12. The Lifestyle Heart trial demonstrated that blocked, even completely blocked, blood vessels could dramatically improve, when patients adhered to a plant-based, zero cholesterol diet, along with exercise and stress management. Interestingly, the control group of this study followed the American Heart Association's recommendations of cutting out butter, switching meat consumption to mostly chicken or fish and they demonstrated no improvement or had actually worsened their cardiac status.

13. Nutrition is The Prescription! There is no reason for anyone to develop heart disease, strokes, Type 2 diabetes, or dementia. To prevent or reverse these and most other chronic diseases, you don't need instruc-

tions from a doctor's prescription pad. The body has an incredible ability to heal itself when properly nourished and when we reduce the toxic foods we eat. A high-nutrient diet is more effective than medications at resolving most medical problems, and promoting a pleasurable, longer and healthier life.

14. Where's the Beef? For years, the USDA Food Pyramid has suggested we consume beef and other animal products in order to get our protein. The USDA suggests approximately 600 calories of beef per day. Instead, remember that vegetables, beans and seeds are also high in protein, so there is no essential need to have animal products at every meal. In fact, broccoli has more protein per calorie than steak. Think about it... cows are vegan, as are gorillas and horses. Trying to lose weight or reduce your cholesterol? Think Greens for health and for building lean muscles. For great health we need to get more protein from nutrient-rich plant sources such as greens, beans, seeds and nuts and less from animal products.

15. Not Milk? An average cow produces 25 times more milk per year than just fifty years ago. Are cows getting bigger? Sure we all need calcium for strong bones, but calcium is just a small part of the story, hundreds of other nutrients are also needed for healthy bones and the quantity of vegetables consumed, not dairy, is the best predictor of bone health. Remember, green vegetables not only have plenty of calcium, but have the other necessary nutrients that build bones. For great health, we should get more calcium from nutrient-rich plant sources such as greens, beans, seeds and nuts and less from dairy products. Our body needs thousands of discovered and undiscovered nutrients that

work synergistically. A higher intake of milk is linked to a higher incidence of both prostate cancer and ovarian cancer.

16. Watch the Olive Oil! One tablespoon of olive oil has 120 calories (all oils do). One-quarter cup has 500 calories. Healthy salads are definitely a way of life for people who want to lose weight or improve health. However, many of the benefits of a salad are lost when the calorie count is increased ten-fold with oil. Flavored vinegars, fruit and nut-based dressings are definitely the way to go. Nuts and seeds, not oil, have shown dramatic protection against heart disease. We need to get more of our fats from these wholesome foods and less from processed oils.

17. Six-A-Day... Not The Way! You have probably heard it's better to eat six small meals a day. That is not ideal. You simply will not need to eat that frequently once your body is well nourished with micronutrients. The body can more effectively detoxify and enhance cell repair when not constantly eating and digesting. Eating right removes cravings and reduces the sensations driving us to eat too frequently and too much. For most people who follow a high-nutrient diet-style, eating when truly hungry means eating three meals a day. For many, two meals and a snack is plenty of food.

COMMON QUESTIONS AND ANSWERS

1. What about Organic Foods?

The effects of ingesting pesticides in the very small amounts present in vegetation are unknown. Every study done to date on the consumption of food and its relation to cancer, though, has shown that the more fruits and vegetables people eat, the less cancer and heart disease they have. Almost all these studies were done on people eating conventionally grown, not organic, produce. So, clearly, the benefit of conventional produce outweighs any hypothetical risks of not eating organically grown produce.

Some scientists argue that humans ingest thousands of natural chemicals that typically have a greater toxicity and are present in higher doses than the very minute amount of pesticide residue that remains on food. Animal studies on the carcinogenic potential in synthetic chemicals are done at doses a thousand-fold higher than what is ingested in food. A high percentage of all chemicals, natural or not, are potentially toxic in high doses—"the dose makes the poison".

Others believe a slight risk may be present, though the risk may be difficult to prove. There certainly is a justifiable concern that some chemicals have increased toxicity and are potentially harmful at lower doses than are used in rodent experiments. No scientist believes that this means we should reduce our consumptions of vegetation, but many (including me) believe it prudent to reduce our exposure to the multiple toxic residues present in our food supply. I certainly advocate avoiding the skins of foods that are reported to have the most pesticide residue. And, of course, all fruits and vegetables should be washed before eating.

See the "Dirty Dozen" list on the following page for the most consistently contaminated produce. These are the foods that would make the most sense to purchase organically grown.

If you are concerned about pesticides and chemicals, keep in mind that animal products, such as dairy and beef, contain the most toxic pesticide residues. Because cows and steers eat large amounts of tainted feed, certain pesticides and dangerous chemicals are found in higher concentrations in animal foods. For example, dioxin, which is predominantly found in fatty meats and dairy products, is one of the most potent toxins linked to several cancers in humans, including lymphomas.[9] By basing your diet on unrefined plant foods, you automatically reduce your exposure to the most dangerous chemicals.

THE "DIRTY DOZEN"

(CONSISTENTLY MOST CONTAMINATED FRUITS AND VEGETABLES)
THE ENVIRONMENTAL WORKING GROUP [10]

RANK		SCORE* (100 = MOST TOXIC)
1	peaches	100
2	apples	93
3	bell peppers	83
4	celery	82
5	nectarines	81
6	strawberries	80
7	cherries	73
8	kale	69
9	lettuce	67
10	imported grapes	66
11	carrots	63
12	pears	63

*Pesticide contamination based on an analysis of 87,000 tests for pesticides on these foods, conducted from 2000 to 2007 by the U.S. Department of Agriculture and the Food and Drug Administration. Nearly all the studies used to create the list test produce after it has been rinsed or peeled. Contamination was measured in six different ways and crops were ranked based on a composite score from all categories

The vegetables *least likely* to have pesticides on them are onions, sweet corn, asparagus, sweet peas, cabbage, eggplant, broccoli, tomatoes, and sweet potatoes. The fruits *least likely* to have pesticide residues on them are avocados, pineapples, mangoes, kiwi, papayas, watermelon and grapefruit. Of course those are all fruits with thicker skins, that we don't usually eat.

2. What about coffee?

Recent research indicates that coffee may not be so bad after all as studies have linked coffee drinking to lower risks of diabetes and Parkinson's disease. So which is it—good or bad? My take on this complicated issue is that one cup of coffee per day is not likely to cause significant risks, but the more you drink over this one cup maximum, the more likely it will interfere with your health.

Recent studies have generally found no connection between coffee and an increased risk of cancer or heart disease. Whereas in the past, it was more suspect. It is thought now that earlier studies didn't always take into account that unhealthy habits such as eating poorly, smoking and not exercising were more common among heavy coffee drinkers. Plus, coffee does contain phenols and flavonoids with some health benefits, but certainly those beneficial phytonutrients can also be ingested from healthy plant foods, not only from a drink that has a stimulant like caffeine in it. Also, keep in mind that coffee accompaniments such as cream and sugar adds saturated fat and empty calories to your diet. Finally, heavy caffeine use—on the order of four to seven cups of coffee a day—can cause problems such as restlessness, anxiety, irritability and sleeplessness, particularly in susceptible individuals.

High consumption of coffee is associated with mild elevations in cholesterol levels. If you are one of those people who eliminate caffeine more slowly from the body two or more cups of coffee a day can increase the risk of heart disease. So, how quickly you metabolize coffee may affect your health risks from coffee.

Caffeine, coffee's main ingredient is a mild addictive stimulant with modest cardiovascular effects such as increased heart rate, increased blood pressure, and occasional irregular heartbeat that should be considered. Studies have been largely inconclusive regarding coffee and its effect on women's health issues such as breast health, cancer, and osteoporosis. But, the negative effects of coffee tend to emerge with excessive use, so it is best to avoid heavy consumption. Heavy caffeine users are at higher risk of cardiac arrhythmias, which can precipitate sudden death.[11] Coffee raises blood pressure and it raises both cholesterol and homocysteine, two risk factors for heart disease.[12]

Besides the slightly increased risks from higher levels of caffeine, especially in susceptible individuals there are other problems. Caffeine is a stimulant. The consumption of caffeine enables you to more comfortably get by on less sleep. Inadequate sleep promotes disease and premature aging.[13] There is no substitute for adequate sleep. Drinking coffee also boosts estrogen levels. Higher levels of estrogen worsen problems like endometriosis, breast pain and menstrual disorders. Increased estrogen levels are also linked to higher risk of breast cancer.[14]

If you are overweight, there is another compelling reason to abstain from coffee. Eliminating your caffeine intake can help you lose weight. Coffee drinkers (tea and cola users too) are drawn to eat more frequently than necessary. They eat extra meals and snacks because they mistake unpleasant caffeine withdrawal symptoms with hunger. They can't tell the difference between true hunger and the discomfort that accompanies caffeine withdrawal.

Decaffeinated coffee also has potentially harmful side effects. It has been found that drinking even moderate amounts of decaffeinated coffee can quadruple a person's risk of developing rheumatoid arthritis.[15] Researchers speculate that organic solvents in the decaf coffee might be the culprit.

In summary, coffee is most like a drug, not a food. Like most drugs it may have some minor benefits, but its toxic effects and resultant risks overwhelm those minor advantages. Caffeine is a stimulant. A healthy later life and long life is most consistently achieved when stimulants and drugs are avoided, meeting our nutritional needs, with as little exposure to toxicity as possible.

3. To Salt or not to Salt?

Sodium is an important mineral that is essential to the body's proper function—however, adding salt (sodium chloride) to food provides us with dangerously high amounts of sodium. The human body was designed to obtain the sodium it needs from natural foods. All salt originates from the ocean—expensive and exotic sea salts are still salt—they contain over 98% sodium chloride. They add sodium to the body, and so they have the same risks as regular table salt. Sea salts may contain small amounts of trace minerals, but the excess sodium is not any less harmful. Also, the amounts of trace minerals in sea salts are insignificant compared to the amounts that can be obtained from natural plant foods. There are no nutritional benefits to consuming any particular type of salt.

The human diet, for millions of years, did not contain any added salt, and provided less than 1000 mg of sodium per day. Populations in pockets of the world that do not salt their food do not have elderly citizens with high blood pressure. Today Americans typically consume 3500 mg of sodium per day. Americans also have a 90% lifetime probability of developing high blood pressure, which is an important risk factor for future cardiovascular events—hypertension is responsible for two-thirds of all strokes.[16] When salt intake is high, excess fluid accumulates in the circulatory system, exerting pressure on the walls of blood vessels, consequently raising blood pressure and overworking the heart. Pumping against this high pressure constantly for many years can cause the heart muscle to enlarge, which can eventually lead to heart failure. Elevated blood pressure is also damaging to the kidneys and increases the risk of hemorrhagic stroke.[17] There are medications designed to improve hypertension, but these offer only marginal protection against cardiovascular disease. Only about one-third of people taking drugs for hypertension have favorable levels of blood pressure.[18] When on these medications, people often think that they are protected and that they can continue their disease-causing lifestyles, which inevitably result in medical tragedies. Adopting a disease-protective diet, rich in micronutrients and free of added salt provides a high level of protection against these conditions that most Americans suffer from as they age—as the harmful effects of their poor lifestyle choices accumulate.

Elevated blood pressure is not the only harmful consequence of high sodium intake—sodium has additional detrimental effects even in the absence of hypertension that contribute to coronary heart disease, asthma, stomach ulcers, and stomach cancer.[19] Excess sodium intake also increases the amount of calcium and other minerals excreted by the body, which could lead to bone loss and osteoporosis.[20] Alarmingly, high sodium intake also correlates with death from all causes in men.[21]

Since most salt comes from processed foods, avoiding added sodium isn't difficult. If you don't use salt, your taste buds adjust with time and your sensitivity to taste salt improves. By avoiding processed and salted foods, you regain your ability to detect and enjoy the subtle flavors in natural foods and actually experience heightened pleasure from foods that are not heavily seasoned. Resist adding salt to foods and purchase salt-free canned goods and soups. If you must salt your food, do so only after it is on the table and you are ready to eat it—it will taste saltier if the salt is right on the surface. Condiments such as ketchup, mustard, soy sauce, teriyaki sauce, and relish are all high in sodium. Use garlic, onion, fresh or dried herbs, spices, lemon or lime juice, or vinegar to flavor food.

The American Heart Association recommends a sodium intake of less than 1500 mg daily. I do not think that is ideal and instruct people ideally to consume less than 1000 mg of sodium a day. Natural foods contain less than 50 mg of sodium per 100 calories. If eating whole grain bread, tomato sauce or any other prepared food, read the label. Aim for less than 200 – 400 mg of added sodium per day. Preferably, choose foods that have less sodium (in mg) than the number of calories per serving to protect your future health. Consuming less sodium is one of the most important things you can do to prevent cardiovascular disease and extend your lifespan.[22]

4. The Red Wine Debate

Moderate drinking has been associated with a lower incidence of coronary heart disease in more than forty prospective studies. This only applies to moderate drinking—defined as one drink or less per day for women, and two drinks or less for men. Excess alcohol is of course harmful—more than moderate alcohol intake is associated with increased fat around the waist and other potential problems, especially increased incidence of cancer.[23]

As a result of these studies, alcohol has been touted as "heart-healthy". However, alcohol does not actually have any beneficial effect on the cardiovascular system; it only inhibits the blood's clotting mechanisms, similar to aspirin. Researchers have found that this interference with blood clotting does grant some protective effect against heart attacks, but this protective effect is valuable only in a person or population consuming a dangerous, heart-disease-promoting diet. Eating a diet rich in unrefined plant foods is health-promoting and effective at preventing heart disease, and then the risks associated with thinning the blood such as hemorrhagic stroke and stomach and intestinal bleeding is not increased. Thinning the blood with alcohol or aspirin has potentially life-threatening risks.

Alcohol consumption also leads to mild withdrawal sensations the next day that are commonly mistaken for hunger. This leads people to eat more than is genuinely necessary, resulting in weight gain. One glass of wine per day is likely insignificant, but I advise against higher levels of alcohol consumption, as it may lead to health problems. For example, even moderate alcohol consumption is linked to higher rates of breast cancer and also higher rates of breast cancer recurrence after diagnosis[24]—since breast cancer is the second leading cause of death in women (second to cardiovascular disease), it is best for women to minimize alcohol consumption in order to reduce these risks. Alcohol is also associated with cardiac arrhythmias, which may lead to sudden cardiac death.[25]

Red wine is the alcoholic beverage most often associated with reduced cardiovascular risk. Red wine does contain some beneficial compounds such as flavonoids and resveratrol, a potent antioxidant in the skin of grapes associated with a number of health benefits. Of course, grapes, raisins, berries, and other plant foods also contain these beneficial compounds. It is not necessary to drink wine to obtain these phytochemicals.

And lastly, the sensible reason the American Heart Association does not recommend people drink wine or other alcoholic beverages is stated below:

> *Drinking more alcohol increases such dangers as alcoholism, high blood pressure, obesity, stroke, breast cancer, suicide and accidents. Also, it's not possible to predict in which people alcoholism will become a problem. Given these and other risks, the American Heart Association cautions people NOT to start drinking if they do not already drink alcohol. Consult your doctor on the benefits and risks of consuming alcohol in moderation.*[26]

I agree, drinking alcohol or one cup of wine is not a major risk, nor is it a major health asset but if consumed in excess; it can develop into a major health risk. Overall, it is safer to eat a diet that will not permit heart disease rather than to rely on alcohol to decrease the potential of blood to clot. The bottom line is that the moderate drinking of alcohol is only an advantage to those who consume an unhealthy diet. There are no protective effects in low risk individuals consuming healthful, plant based diets with resultant low cholesterol levels. It is wiser to avoid the detrimental effects of alcohol completely and protect yourself from heart disease with nutritional excellence.

5. Do I need Vitamins?

Since most people's diets are not ideal and individual absorption and utilization varies from person to person, it makes sense to recommend that all people take a high-quality multivitamin/multimineral to avoid micronutrient deficiencies. It is important to ensure adequate levels of essential micronutrients, such as vitamin D, vitamin B12, zinc, iodine, and DHA. The judicious use of supplements can be utilized to offer nutritional insurance, but many nutritional supplements can bring about more harm than good - more is not always better. People can easily hurt themselves with too much supplementation.

Typical multivitamins may expose you to extra nutrients that you do not need and can even be toxic. Excessive quantities of some vitamins and minerals can be toxic or have long term negative health effects. Some forms are more absorbable and useful to our bodies then others. The goal is to supplement intelligently. The following are potentially dangerous supplements that are routinely added to most multivitamins.

Beta-carotene, Vitamin A, and Vitamin E. There are risks associated with consuming more beta-carotene and vitamin A than what we naturally receive in our diets. Ingesting vitamin A or beta-carotene in isolation from supplements can potentially increase cancer risk by interfering with the absorption of other carotenoids with anti-cancer properties, like lutein and lycopene.[27] Beta-carotene supplements are poor substitutes for the broad assortment of carotenoid compounds found in plants. It is much safer and healthier to consume food sources of beta-carotene, like spinach, kale and carrots, which also contain several additional carotenoids as well as hundreds of other beneficial phytochemicals.

Since beta-carotene gets converted into vitamin A by your body, there is no reason a person eating a reasonably healthy diet should require any extra vitamin A. There is solid research revealing that supplemental vitamin A induces calcium loss in the urine, contributing to osteoporosis.[28] Too much vitamin A from supplements during pregnancy is associated with cardiac birth defects.[29] On top of these risks, a recent meta-analysis found an increased risk of mortality in people who took supplemental vitamin A, beta-carotene, or vitamin E.[30]

Iron and copper. Iron and copper serve vital biological functions, but as we age excess amounts of these metals may build up and become toxic. The most common culprits of iron and copper excess are red meat and multivitamins. Iron is crucial for oxygen transport, and both iron and copper are essential for the proper function of several chemical reactions in several of the body's cells and tissues. The human body evolved to store excess iron and copper to fuel these reactions in case of extreme conditions like bleeding or famine. However, their accumulation over time may be detrimental because both metals are involved in generating oxidative stress, a byproduct of energy production, which contributes to chronic diseases—specifically cardiovascular disease and brain disorders like Alzheimer's Disease.[31] There are appropriate times to supplement with iron, however—when there is a deficiency or an increased biological need, such as in pregnancy.

Folic acid. The synthetic folic acid found in supplements is chemically different from food folate, which is abundant in green vegetables like spinach, romaine lettuce, collards, and broccoli. Folate is especially important for women of childbearing age, to prevent against birth defects. However, women who take synthetic folic acid in multivitamins or prenatal vitamins may be at increased risk of breast cancer.[32] Folic acid supplementation also raises the risk of prostate and colorectal cancers.[33] Luckily, we don't need to get folic acid from vitamins, because folate is plentiful in green vegetables. Folate in its natural form protects against breast and prostate cancers.[34] Getting folate from food ensures that we do not get too much, since it comes naturally packaged in balance with other micronutrients.

In spite of the huge volume of solid information documenting the deleterious effects of these supplements, it is still difficult to find a multivitamin that does not contain these substances. For more information on potentially harmful supplements, please visit:

www.drfuhrman.com/library/harmful_vitamins.aspx

For recommendations on appropriate vitamins and supplements, please visit my Vitamin Advisor:

www.drfuhrman.com/shop/VAdvisor.aspx

Remember, dietary supplements are indeed supplements, not substitutes for a healthy diet.

6. Sugar: Enough is Enough!
So which sweeteners are best?

Primates are the only mammal that can sense sweet tastes. Fruit is an essential part of the human diet. We have such a large area of our tongue to taste sweets and a natural inclination to enjoy them. Our natural sweet tooth has a purpose —sweets from fresh fruits and other plant substances provide us not just with carbohydrates for energy but also with a large assortment of phytochemicals and other substances that prevent illness.

Unfortunately, in our society, our natural primate desire for sweets is typically satisfied by consuming products containing refined sugars—candy bars, soda, and ice cream—instead of fresh fruit. The American Heart Association released a statement in 2009 reporting that the typical American adult now consumes an unbelievable 22 teaspoons of added sugar each day—even more troubling was that teens were found to consume even more added sugar—34 teaspoons per day.[35]

Refined sugars cause us to be malnourished in direct proportion to how much of them we consume. They are partially to blame for the high cancer and heart attack rates we see in America. Refined sugars include table sugar (sucrose), milk sugar (lactose), honey, brown sugar, high-fructose corn syrup, molasses, corn sweeteners, maple syrup and fruit juice concentrates—to your body, they are all the same—empty calories. Even the fruit juices that many children drink are a poor quality food with no significant nutrient density—juices don't compare to the real fruit. White rice, white bread, and pasta are no different than sugar once we put them in our mouths—they are deficient in nutrients and are absorbed too rapidly—empty calories just like sugar, raising our blood sugar and insulin levels. Also the lack of nutrients in these refined foods means that these foods will not satisfy our appetites—this leads to over-eating, which contributes to obesity, diabetes, cardiovascular disease, and cancers

Refined sugars and nutrient-depleted processed sweets—deficient in fiber, phytonutrients, vitamins and minerals—are a poor substitute for fresh fruit. These foods are harmful, but even more harmful is that we are missing hundreds of valuable phytochemicals when we eat these nutrient-deficient desserts instead of fresh fruit.

Fresh fruits are natural, nutrient-rich, health-promoting foods. Researchers have discovered substances in fruits—especially blueberries and strawberries—that have unique effects on preventing aging and deterioration of the brain.[36] Adding more fresh fruit to the diet can decrease the risk of diabetes.[37] Some fruits, especially blueberries, are rich in anthocyanins and other compounds that have anti-aging effects.[38] Apple consumption is associated with decreased risk of colorectal cancer.[39] Eating citrus fruits decreases the risk of all cancers of the digestive tract.[40] Overall fruit consumption has been shown in numerous studies to offer our strongest protection against several cancers: oral and esophageal, lung, prostate, colorectal, and pancreatic cancer.[41]

How much fruit your children eat is also a strong determinant of their future health—a sixty-year study of about 5,000 participants found that those who were in the highest quartile of fruit consumption during childhood were found to have 38% lower incidence of all types of cancer as adults.[42]

Eating fruit instead of empty-calorie refined sugar is vital to your health and longevity. Sadly, according to the American Heart Association, Americans typically eat less than 2 servings of fruit per day—I recommend 4 - 6 servings of these nutrient-dense treats per day for excellent health.

In our house, not only do we enjoy fruit in its natural state, but we also whip up frozen fruits to make fantastic sorbets and creamy desserts. Do you think that your sweet tooth can't be satisfied by fruit? You can make delicious desserts without using refined sugars—try this one: a little dried mango, soaked overnight in soy or hemp milk, blended up in a high quality blender with frozen mango, a little lemon and shredded coconut for a real treat for the entire family. You can substitute many other fruits in place of the mango.

TEST YOUR KNOWLEDGE

1. Dr. Fuhrman's health equation for life extension and heart disease protection is Health = _____ divided by calories.

2. Why don't people who switch from red meat to chicken or fish see a substantial change in their cholesterol level or a reduction in cardiac events?

   _____

   _____

   _____

3. Name at least three health problems that excessive salt intake increases your risk of getting?

   1) _____

   2) _____

   3) _____

4. Normally a low cholesterol level is protective against heart disease and stroke and yet under what circumstances can a low cholesterol level actually increase your chances of a hemorrhagic stroke?

_____

5. List 6 out of the 9 contributors of heart disease.

   1) _____

   2) _____

   3) _____

   4) _____

   5) _____

   6) _____

6. The drive to overeat is mainly caused by _____ deficiency.

7. List the 5 categories of unlimited foods. These are the foods that I recommend eating large amounts of—they are high volume, nutrient dense, low calorie foods.

   1) _____

   2) _____

   3) _____

   4) _____

   5) _____

8. What is the list of non-green, unlimited vegetables?

_____

_____

_____

_____

9. List 3 items at or near the top of the caloric density scores and 3 items at or near the bottom of the caloric density list.

TOP

1) _____

2) _____

3) _____

BOTTOM

1) _____

2) _____

3) _____

10. Describe what toxic hunger is. Give three common symptoms that occur during toxic hunger.

_____

1) _____

2) _____

3) _____

11. Explain why diets based on portion control or calorie counting doesn't work.

_____

_____

_____

_____

_____

12. Give at least 2 reasons why eating a lot a fish in order to supposedly get their healthy fatty acid benefits can back-fire and cause your health to suffer.

1) _____

2) _____

13. Protein deficiency in the United States is very rare no matter whether you eat animal protein or are a strict vegan and eat only plant-based protein—explain why this is.

_____

_____

_____

_____

14. List 4 foods that are high in plant-protein and can easily replace the animal protein one might be consuming right now.

1) _____

2) _____

3) _____

4) _____

15. Explain why one does not need to mix and match plant derived proteins in order to form "complete" proteins as long as they eat a healthy plant based diet with a variety of wholesome foods.

_____

_____

_____

16. Besides heart attacks and strokes a person on a high salt diet who develops high blood pressure has an increased risk for:

a) dementia

b) eye disease and blindness

c) thickening and enlargement of the heart

d) kidney failure

e) heart arrhythmia

f) all of the above

17. When eating out at a restaurant, besides condiments, list 3 items that typically contain the highest salt content.

1) _____

2) _____

3) _____

18. List 4 things you can do today to help bring your blood pressure to a normal range.

1) _____

2) _____

3) _____

4) _____

19. If one follows a completely vegetarian/vegan diet without fortified foods and doesn't work outdoors, which two important vitamins should be supplemented?

1) _____

2) _____

20. List 3 vegetarian sources of omega 3 fatty acids.

1) _____

2) _____

3) _____

21. GOMBS is an acronyms to help you remember the most powerful anti-cancer foods. What are they?

G _____

O _____

M _____

B _____

S _____

22. Which food has the highest percentage (on a per calorie basis) of saturated fat? _____

23. How is a bagel similar to a piece of chicken?

_____

24. Getting rid of excess _____ is the first step in the recovery from diabetes.

25. _____ vegetables contain glucosinolates, which when the vegetables are chopped or chewed, are converted into powerful anti-cancer compounds called isothiocyanates.

THE LAST WORD

As long as you are alive, you can improve your health and prolong your life. Our health is our most precious and important possession we have and we should never give up our efforts to improve and maintain excellent health. We graduate from school; high school, college, even professional school (such as medical school) and the most important information we should have learned to protect our life and health destiny is not imparted to us. Social and economic forces acting against healthy eating, as well as the addictive nature of unhealthy foods, have taken over the minds and actions of most Americans. Slow suicide from overeating low-nutrient food is the norm.

I am here to tell you that my more than 25 years of experience helping people regain their health and their weight has taught me that healthy living is a blessing that makes life more pleasurable and fun. Plus, food doesn't taste that good once you are in the coffin. Congratulations on your efforts to better your health. We are on this road to better health together. Society's norms, with its reliance on drugs and the disease-promoting properties of the standard American diet have negative influences on our health. By working together and supporting each other we can achieve better health, make what we eat taste great and enjoy a better quality of life.

Visit me at DrFuhrman.com

**Consider joining our member center
for more support and camaraderie.**

Follow our blog conversations at DiseaseProof.com

I LOOK FORWARD TO HEARING ABOUT YOUR SUCCESS
AND HOPE YOU ACHIEVE INCREDIBLE HEALTH.

Score yourself with 4 points
for each question answered correctly.

1. Nutrients

2. Consuming animal protein, in addition to saturated fat and cholesterol, also raises cholesterol levels.

3. 3 of the following:

    Hypertension

    Stroke

    Heart disease

    Asthma

    Kidney disease

    Osteoporosis

    Gastric ulcers

    Gastric cancer

4. Under the conditions of high salt consumption and resulting high blood pressure, having a low cholesterol level actually increases the likelihood of hemorrhagic stroke.

5. Six of the following:

    Cigarette smoking

    Abnormal blood lipids

    High blood pressure

    Diabetes

    Waist fat (waist circumference greater than 40" for men; greater than 35" for women)

Stress

Insufficient daily fruit consumption

Insufficient daily vegetable consumption

Lack of daily exercise

6. Micronutrient

7. Five categories of unlimited foods:

   Raw vegetables

   Cooked green vegetables

   Cooked non-green, non-starchy vegetables

   Fresh fruit

   Beans

8. Cauliflower, carrots, eggplant, mushrooms, onions, tomatoes, peppers, beets

9. High caloric density foods: oil, potato chips/French fries, meat, cheese, white bread

   Low caloric density foods: green vegetables, non-starchy non-green vegetables, fresh fruit, beans

10. Toxic hunger is the name for the sensations most people mistakenly consider hunger. Toxic hunger is a constellation of symptoms that illustrates a physical addiction to an unhealthy diet. They are signs of the body's need to detoxify during the heightened cleansing available after digestion ceases. Symptoms of toxic hunger include headaches, weakness, stomach cramping, lightheadedness, esophageal spasms, growling stomach, and irritability.

11. Diets based on portion control or calorie counting don't work because nutrient inadequacy is a factor that drives hunger – even if the body's requirement for calories has been met, hunger will still be experienced if nutrient requirements are not met.

12. Two reasons why eating fish to get their healthy fatty acids can cause your health to suffer: 1-fish contains pollutants such as mercury that can be detrimental to health, 2-fish is still animal protein, which is high in calories and low in micronutrients, and will tend to raise cholesterol levels.

13. Every food gets its calories from some combination of protein, fat, and carbohydrate. Protein is not only found in animal foods - most of the calories in green vegetables, for example, come from protein. If you consume enough calories (regardless of the proportion of animal to plant foods), naturally you will consume enough protein.

14. Foods high in plant protein: seeds (sunflower, hemp, sesame, pumpkin, etc.), nuts, beans, and green vegetables.

15. Every single essential amino acid does not need to be consumed in each meal. Some plant foods have more of certain amino acids than others, so over the course of a day, eating a variety of plant foods will provide adequate amounts of all of the essential amino acids.

16. All of the above (f)

17. Soups, sauces, and salad dressings

18. Four of the following: restrict sodium, restrict animal products, avoid refined carbohydrates, avoid caffeine, avoid alcohol, eat more vegetables, eat more fresh fruit.

19. Vitamin D, Vitamin B12

20. Three of the following: walnuts, flaxseed, chia seeds, hemp seeds

21. GOMBS: greens, onions, mushrooms, beans and berries, seeds

22. Cheese

23. Both a bagel and a piece of chicken are high in calories and low in micronutrients.

24. Body fat

25. Cruciferous

References

1   National Center for Health Statistics, NHANES data on the Prevalence of Overweight and Obesity Among Adults- United States, 2003-2004, April 2006. http://www.cdc.gov/nchs/fastats/overwt.htm

2   Instutute of Medicine of the National Academies. Focus on Childhood Obesity. http://www.iom.edu/cms/22593.aspx

3   American Heart Association. Heart Disease and Stroke Statistics. 2009 Update. http://www.americanheartassociation.org/presenter. jhtml?identifer=128.

Centers for Disease Control and Prevention. US Department of Health and Human Services. Diabetes: At-a-Glance 2009. www.cdc.gov/ nccdphp/publications/aag/ddt.htm. American Cancer Society. Cancer Facts & Figures. 2003. Accessed at http://www.cancer.org/downloads/ Stt/500809web.pdf on 9/28/09. National Osteoporosis Foundation. Osteoporosis Disease Statistics: Fast Facts. http://www.nof.org/ awareness2/images/fast_facts

4   Must A, Spadiano J, Coakley EH, et al. The disease burden associated with overweight and obesity. JAMA 1999; 282(16):1523-9.Allison DB, Fontaine KR, Manson JE, et al.   Annual deaths attributable to obesity in the United States. JAMA 1999 282 (16):1530-38. Adams K, Schatzkin A, Harris TB, et al. Overweight, Obesity and Mortality in a Large Prospective Cohort of Persons 50-71 Years old. N Engl J Med. 2006;355:763-778.

5   Heron M, Tejada-Vera B. National Office of Vital Statistics, Deaths: Leading Causes for 2005; Vol. 58, No. 8,2009. http://www.cdc.gov/nchs/ data/nvsr/nvsr58/nvsr58_08.pdf

6   National Center for Health Statistics, Health, United States, 2004 with Chartbook, Hyattsville, MD: 2005. http://www.cdc.gov/nchs/ pressroom/04news/hus04.htm

7   Campbell TC, Junshi C. Diet and chronic degenerative diseases: perspectives from China. Am J Clin Nutr 1994 May;59(5 Suppl):1153S-1161S.

8   Steinmetz KA, Potter JD. Vegetables, fruit, and cancer prevention: a review. J Am Diet Assoc. 1996 Oct;96(10):1027-39.

Genkinger JM, Platz EA, Hoffman SC, et al. Fruit, vegetable, and antioxidant intake and all-cause, cancer, and cardiovascular disease mortality in a community-dwelling population in Washington County, Maryland. Am J Epidemiol. 2004 Dec 15;160(12):1223-33.

9   Steenland K, Bertazzi P, Baccarelli A, Kogevinas M. Dioxin revisited: developments since the 1997 IARC classification of dioxin as a human carcinogen. Environ Health Perspect. 2004 Sep;112(13):1265-8.

EPA report ratchets up dioxin peril. 2000. Washington Post, May.

10   Environmental Working Group, Shoppers Guide to Pesticides. http://www.foodnews.org/reduce.php, Date accessed: February 11, 2010.

11   Melita A, Jain AC, Mehta MC, Billie M. Caffeine and cardiac arrhythmias, An experimental study in dogs with review of literature. Acta Cardiol 1997;52(3);273-283.

12   Nurminen MI, Niittymen L, Retterstol I, et al. Coffee, caffeine, and blood pressure: a critical review. Eur J Clin Nutr 1999;53(11):831-839. Christensen B, Mosdol A, Retterstol I, et al. Abstention from filtered coffee reduces the concentration of plasma homocysteine and serum cholesterol-a randomized controlled trial. Am J Clin Nutr 2001;74(3);302-307.

13   Spiegel K, Leproult R, Van Cauter EV. Impact of sleep debt on metabolic and endocrine function. Lancet 1999;354(9188);1435-1439.

14   Lucero J, Harlow BI, Berbieri RI, et al. Early follicular phase hormone levels in relation to patterns of alcohol, tobacco and coffee use. Fertile Steril 2001;76(4):723-729.

15   Mikuls TR, Cerhan JR, Criswell LA et al. Coffee, tea and caffeine consumption and risk of rheumatoid arthritis: results from the Iowa Women's Health Study. Arthritis & Rheumatism 2002;46(1):83-91.

16   Luke RG. Transactions of the American Clinical and Climatological Assocation, Vol. 118, 2007. President's Address: Salt – too much of a good thing?

17   American Society of Nephrology: http://asn-online.org

Yano K, Reed MD, MacLean CJ.. Serum Cholesterol and Hemorrhagic Stroke in the Honolulu Heart Program. Stroke 1989;20(11):1460-1465

18 Luke RG. Transactions of the American Clinical and Climatological Assocation, Vol. 118, 2007. President's Address: Salt – too much of a good thing?

19 Tuomilehto J, Jousilahti P, Rastenyte D, et al. Urinary sodium excretion and cardiovascular mortality in Finland: a prospective study. Lancet 2001;357:848-851

Burney P. A diet rich in sodium may potentiate asthma. Epidemiologic evidence for a new hypothesis. Chest 1987;91 (2 Suppl):143s-148s

Tsugane S, Sasazuki S. Diet and the risk of gastric cancer. Gastric Cancer 2007;10(2):75-83

20 Itoh R, Suyama Y. Sodium excretion in relation to calcium and hydroxyproline excretion in a healthy Japanese population. Am J Clin Nutr 1996; 63(5):735-40. Nowson CA, Patchett A, Wattanapenpaiboon N. The effects of a low-sodium base-producing diet including red meat compared with a high-carbohydrate, low-fat diet on bone turnover markers in women aged 45-75 years. Br J Nutr. 2009 Oct;102(8):1161-70. Teucher B, Dainty JR, Spinks CA. Sodium and bone health: impact of moderately high and low salt intakes on calcium metabolism in postmenopausal women. J Bone Miner Res. 2008 Sep;23(9):1477-85.

21 Ito Tuomilehto J, Jousilahti P, Rastenyte D, et. al. Urinary sodium excretion and cardiovascular mortality in Finland: a prospective study. Lancet 2001;357(9259):848-51.

22 National High Blood Pressure Education Program, National Heart, Lung, and Blood Institute. National Institutes of Health. "National High Blood Pressure Education Program Working Group report on primary prevention of hypertension." Arch Intern Med 1993;153:186-208

23 Ferreira MG, Valente JG, Gonçalves-Silva RM, Sichieri R. Alcohol consumption and abdominal fat in blood donors. Rev Saude Publica. 2008 Dec;42(6):1067-73. Sesso HD, Cook NR, Buring JE, et al.. Alcohol consumption and the risk of hypertension in women and men. Hypertension. 2008 Apr;51(4):1080-7.

24 Phend, C. MedPage Today. SABCS: Moderate Drinking Boosts Breast Cancer Recurrence. http://www.medpagetoday.com/MeetingCoverage/SABCS/17444

Singletary KW, Gapstur SM. Alcohol and breast cancer: review of epidemiologic and experimental evidence and potential mechanisms. JAMA. 2001 Nov7;286(17):2143-51.

25 George A, Figueredo VM. Alcohol and arrhythmias: a comprehensive review. J Cardiovasc Med (Hagerstown). 2010 Apr;11(4):221-8.

26 American Heart Association: Alcohol, Wine, and Cardiovascular Disease. http://www.americanheart.org/presenter.jhtml?identifier=4422

27 Mayne ST. Beta-carotene, carotenoids, and disease prevention in humans. FASEB J. 1996 May;10(7):690-701.

28 Melhus H, Michaëlsson K, Kindmark A, et al. Excessive dietary intake of vitamin A is associated with reduced bone mineral density and increased risk for hip fracture. Ann Intern Med. 1998 Nov 15;129(10):770-8.

29 Botto LD, Loffredo C, Scanlon KS, et al. Vitamin A and cardiac outflow tract defects. Epidemiology. 2001Sep;12(5):491-6.

30 Bjelakovic G, Nikolova D, Gluud LL, et al. Antioxidant supplements for prevention of mortality in healthy participants and patients with various diseases. Cochrane Database Syst Rev. 2008 Apr 16;(2):CD007176.

31 Brewer GJ. Iron and Copper Toxicity in Diseases of Aging, Particularly Atherosclerosis and Alzheimer's Disease. Exp Biol Med 232 (2): 323. 2007

32 Charles D, Ness AR, Campbell D, et al. Taking folate in pregnancy and risk of maternal breast cancer. BMJ. 2004 Dec 11;329(7479):1375-6.

33 Figueiredo JC, Grau MV, Haile RW, et al. Folic acid and risk of prostate cancer: results

from a randomized clinical trial. J Natl Cancer Inst. 2009 Mar 18;101(6):432-5.

Fife J, Raniga S, Hider PN, Frizelle FA. Folic acid supplementation and colorectal cancer risk: a meta-analysis. Colorectal Dis. 2011 Feb;13(2):132-7.

34 Sellers TA, Kushi LH, Cerhan JR, et al. Dietary folate intake, alcohol, and risk of breast cancer in a prospective study of postmenopausal women. Epidemiology. 2001Jul;12(4):420-8.

Charles D, Ness AR, Campbell D, et al. Taking folate in pregnancy and risk of maternal breast cancer. BMJ. 2004 Dec 11;329(7479):1375-6.

35 Johnson RK, Appel LJ, Brands M, et al.; American Heart Association Nutrition Committee of the Council on Nutrition, Physical Activity, and Metabolism and the Council on Epidemiology and Prevention. Dietary sugars intake and cardiovascular health: a scientific statement from the American Heart Association. Circulation. 2009 Sep15;120(11):1011-20.

36 Joseph JA, Shukitt-Hale B, Willis LM. Grape juice, berries, and walnuts affect brain aging and behavior. J Nutr. 2009 Sep;139(9):1813S-7S.

37 Bazzano LA, Li TY, Joshipura KJ, Hu FB. Intake of fruit, vegetables, and fruit juices and risk of diabetes in women. Diabetes Care. 2008 Jul;31(7):1311-7.

38 Cao G, Shukitt-Hale B, Bickford PC, et al. Hyperoxia-induced changes in antioxidant capacity and the effect of dietary antioxidants, J Appl Physiol 1999;86(6):1817-22.

39 Jedrychowski W, Maugeri U, Popiela T, et al. Case-control study on beneficial effect of regular consumption of apples on colorectal cancer risk in a population with relatively low intake of fruits and vegetables. Eur J Cancer Prev. 2010 Jan;19(1):42-7.

40 Foschi R, Pelucchi C, Dal Maso L, et al. Citrus fruit and cancer risk in a network of case-control studies. Cancer Causes Control. 2010 Feb;21(2):237-42.

41 Block G, Paterson, B, Sabar A. Fruit,Vegetables and Cancer Prevention: a review of epidemiological evidence. Nutr Cancer 1992;18 (1):1-29. van Duijnhoven FJ, Bueno-De-Mesquita HB, Ferrari P, et al. Fruit, vegetables, and colorectal cancer risk: the European Prospective Investigation into Cancer and Nutrition. Am J Clin Nutr. 2009 May;89(5):1441-52.

42 Maynard M, Gunnell D, Emmett P, et al. Fruit, vegetables and antioxidants in childhood and risk of cancer: the Boyd Orr cohort. J Epidimiol Community Health 2003;57:219-225.

NOTES